The B

The Norton Gazette

Dominic Barker

Illustrated by John Bradley

OXFORD

Chapter 1

Day:	Monday
Time:	8:15 am
Location:	Jack Rico's bedroom

Meet Jack Rico. Age 10. Ace reporter. He looks in the mirror. Hair – too flat. Shirt – too neat. He spikes his hair and untucks his shirt. He grabs his notebook and his pen, opens his bedroom door and heads for the kitchen. "Today is the day I get to break a big story," he tells himself.

Jack's dream is to get a report he's written in *The Norton Gazette*. All he needs to do is find the right person and ask the right questions.

"You're going to be late for school," shouts his mum.

Jack runs down the stairs. He wouldn't be late for school if he had a new bike, but his mum won't let him have one.

"Can I have a new bike?" Jack asks.

His mum doesn't say anything. But she sighs. She's been asked that question before.

"I said, 'Can I have a new bike?'" repeats Jack.

His mum shakes her head.

"Why?"

"Because," says his mum.

"BOY NOT GIVEN GOOD ENOUGH ANSWER BY MOTHER," says Jack, who sometimes talks in headlines.

"It's the only answer you're getting," says his mum. "Sit down and eat your toast."

"Where's the jam?"

"We've run out. You'll have to make do with butter."

"BOY DENIED TOPPING OF CHOICE BY PARENT," observes Jack.

Chapter 2

Day:	Monday
Time:	9:10am
Location:	Room 10, Norton School

Jack is sitting next to Molly, his best friend. She doesn't look too happy. "BEST FRIEND IN SAD FACE SHOCK," comments Jack. "What's up?"

Molly plonks a copy of *The Norton Gazette* on to the desk.

Deadly bug shuts pool

Terrified lifeguards rushed to shut down Norton Swimming Pool yesterday after health officer, Mr Arthur Pribit, discovered traces of a deadly bug. He commented, "I was doing routine tests on water samples when I spotted a strange result. There were signs of Cryptosporidiosis which can cause illness or even death." The pool was shut immediately and will stay closed until further notice.

**The Gazette says:
Well done, Arthur!**

6

"Great story," says Jack.

"Glad you're seeing the good side," says Molly sarcastically.

"What's the matter?"

"The pool is where I train. There isn't another one for miles. It's the Under-11s County Championship in two weeks. If the pool stays shut, I've got no chance of winning."

"A follow-up story," says Jack, reaching for his notebook. "GIRL'S SWIMMING CAREER DESTROYED BY DEADLY BUG. I'll write it and take it to the *Gazette* after school. I knew this would be the day I'd finally get a story printed."

"I'm glad losing my chance in the championship makes you so happy."

"I'm not happy about it," says Jack. "But it's the news. I've got to report it. Just answer a few questions."

He picks up his pen.

"How does it feel to have your swimming career ruined before it's even begun?" Jack asks bluntly. Perhaps a little too bluntly.

Molly gives Jack a furious look.

"I'm not answering that," she snaps. "Report something that can get the pool re-opened if you want to be any help."

She stomps off to feed Gimli, the school hamster.

Chapter 3

Day:	Monday
Time:	4:35 pm
Location:	Offices of the Norton Gazette

"Another story, Jack?"

It's Veronica. Veronica is eighteen and a trainee reporter on the paper. She has to write all the stories nobody else wants to.

Jack nods. "It's a follow-up story about the pool. I'm waiting for Mr Richardson."

Veronica looks concerned. "He's in a bad mood today," she says. "Somebody spelt the mayor's name wrong on page two. She's been on the phone complaining all afternoon. Try another time maybe."

Jack doesn't want to go. This could be his big chance.

"I really think you should go," says Veronica.

But it's too late. The door of the Editor's office opens and a short round man with a moustache stalks out. Jeremy Richardson spots Jack straight away.

"What are you doing here again, Rico?" he demands. "This is a newspaper, not a playground."

"I've got a …"

"Don't tell me," says Richardson. "You've got another story."

Jack nods.

"And you expect me to waste my time reading it?"

"It might be quite good, Mr Richardson," suggests Veronica.

"Good?" snaps Richardson. "Don't you tell me what good is. I nearly had the front-page story on *The Daily World* once. That's no local paper. That's the biggest-selling paper in the whole country. *I'm* the one in this office who decides what good is."

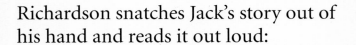

Richardson snatches Jack's story out of his hand and reads it out loud:

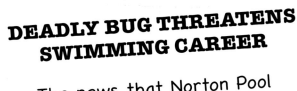

DEADLY BUG THREATENS SWIMMING CAREER

The news that Norton Pool is closed has ruined the training plans of Molly Green (aged 10) of Norton School. She was favourite to win the 50m freestyle but can no longer practise. Now she fears she will be defeated in the Under-11s County Championships. Molly was too upset to comment and was last seen crying on the school hamster.

"Do you want to print it?" Jack asks hopefully.

"Print it?" repeats Richardson. "This is the worst story I've ever read, Rico."

"Don't say that, Mr Richardson," protests Veronica.

"Don't tell *me* what to say and what not to say. There's nothing in this story. She might win, she might lose. You haven't even got a quote from her. There's no drama here, Rico."

"She wouldn't answer my questions," explains Jack, "so I put in the bit about crying on the hamster to make the reader sympathise with her."

"Crying on a hamster?" shouts Richardson. "That's not news. Eating a hamster is news. Crying on one is just weird." He scrunches the story into an ugly ball and throws it expertly into the bin. "I don't want to see you back here," he says pointing a stubby finger at Jack. "Some people can write stories and some people can't. And you, Rico, are one of the people who can't." Richardson stomps back into his office and slams the door.

Jack can't believe it. He thought the story had everything – hope, sport … hamsters.

"BOY'S DREAMS BROKEN BY CRUEL EDITOR," says Jack.

"Perhaps this will make you feel better," says Veronica, taking something out of her pocket.

"What is it?"

"A mini tape recorder. You can use it to tape interviews."

"Are you sure?"

"Yeah. I've got two."

"BOY JUMPS FOR JOY AT SURPRISE GIFT!" says Jack. "Thanks."

"Better luck next time!"

Chapter 4

Day:	Tuesday
Time:	9:10 am
Location:	Assembly hall, Norton School

"Settle down, children," says Miss Targett. "Today is a special day." Miss Targett is wearing her best red suit.

Molly sits down next to Jack. "HAS EX-SWIMMER FORGIVEN BEST FRIEND?" Jack asks.

Molly doesn't say anything.

"I'll take that as 'no comment,'" Jack says.

"Jack Rico! Are you talking?" shouts Miss Targett. Everybody turns to look at Jack.

"Are we on the record?" he asks Miss Targett.

"I beg your pardon, Rico?"

"On the record, I wasn't talking," explains Jack. "Off the record, I was."

Miss Target gives Jack one of her Stares.

"You're very lucky, Jack Rico. We've got a special guest here so I'm not going to tell you off. But I've got my eye on you."

Jack decides to be good. At least until she takes that eye off him.

"Today," says Miss Targett, "we're very fortunate to have a visitor. Please welcome Mr Howard, owner of UltraGym."

Mr Howard walks to the front of the assembly hall. He's wearing a blue shirt but no tie and the biggest smile Jack has ever seen. The only time he's seen more teeth was in a shark's mouth.

"Hi, kids!"

"Hello, Mr Howard," they chorus back.

"No, no," says Mr Howard. "Don't call me Mr Howard. Call me Dave. I want you, your parents and your teachers to think of me as a friend. I'm everybody's friend."

"MAN WITH BIG TEETH WANTS TO BE YOUR FRIEND," whispers Jack to Molly.

Molly smiles and then remembers she's angry with Jack and stops.

"Today I want to talk to you about health, exercise and UltraGym," says Dave. "UltraGym has just opened and it's a state-of-the-art fitness centre. It's very important that you and your parents get lots of exercise and at UltraGym we aim to provide that. Now that the town swimming pool is closed…"

Molly sighs regretfully.

"…UltraGym has the only swimming pool for miles around. So tell your parents they should join immediately. UltraGym is great value for money. Thank you."

Miss Targett stands up. "Aren't you forgetting something, Mr Howard?"

"Am I?"

Miss Targett gives Mr Howard one of her stares.

"Oh, yes," he says. "We at UltraGym believe in children doing exercise and being healthy and growing up to be adults who join UltraGym. Therefore we are donating a hundred pounds worth of high-quality sports equipment to the school. Remember, at UltraGym we care. Thank you." Dave Howard and his big smile sit down.

"I'm sure we'd all like to say thank you to Mr Howard for his generous donation, wouldn't we, children?" says Miss Targett.

The children know what they have to do.

"Thank you, Mr Howard," they all chorus obediently.

"Now," says Miss Targett, "please wait quietly. Mr Richardson from the local paper is here to take a picture."

Mr Richardson walks forward, clutching a camera in one hand and a notebook and pencil in the other.

He seems very different to the man who was so horrible to Jack yesterday. "Hello, children," he says cheerfully. "Mr Howard has put a large ad in the paper this week for UltraGym so we want to make sure there's a good story and picture to go with it. Mr Howard, could you stand in front of the children? Everybody smile – one … two … three …" FLASH!

Moments later Dave Howard and Mr Richardson were getting into their cars and driving away.

Chapter 5

Day: Wednesday
Time: 10:15 am
Location: Locker room,
          Norton School

Norton's kids say "yes" to UltraGym

Yesterday was great at Norton School. Children cheered when Dave Howard, local businessman, announced he would be donating sports equipment worth thousands of pounds to the school. One child, Jack Rico, said, "Mr Howard is my hero. Everyone should join UltraGym." His friend Molly added, "I'm glad the local swimming pool is shut. Now I can make my parents take me to UltraGym." Friendly Dave stayed behind after assembly, signing autographs for the children. "I don't mind," says Dave. "I'll do anything to keep kids healthy."

The *GAZETTE* says: Dave's a local hero.

"That didn't happen," says Jack, reading the article in disbelief. "I never said that."

"Talking to yourself, Rico?"

Jack looks up. All the other boys are already changed and gone. Standing over him is Mr Morris, the PE teacher.

"I was just …"

"Reading," says Mr Morris. "This is PE. Time to stop reading and start running. You can carry out this bag. It's got the new equipment from UltraGym."

Jack picks up the bag. It's heavy.

"BOY SUES SCHOOL AFTER INJURING BACK," he mutters.

Outside, Jack's class is lined up on the playground. "Today we get to use the new equipment sent by UltraGym," Mr Morris tells them. He reaches into the bag and pulls out a basketball. "Wonderful!" he says. "We need a new basketball." He bounces it on the ground. It doesn't bounce back.

"It's got a puncture," says Molly.

Mr Morris looks at the flat basketball with disappointment. "Probably got put in by accident," he says. "What else is in here?"

He tries again. "I can feel a tennis racket," he says. "We could really do with … oh!" Mr Morris pulls out a tennis racket. Half the strings are missing. He yanks out a discus. It's warped. "This is all rubbish." Mr Morris dumps the bag on the ground.

"Excuse me, Mr Morris."

"What is it, Rico?"

"Miss Targett says you shouldn't drop rubbish in the playground."

Chapter 6

Day:	Wednesday
Time:	4:45pm
Location:	Offices of The Norton Gazette

"Veronica, I told you not to let him in here again!"

"He said it was important, Mr Richardson."

"I wanted to ask you about the story in today's *Gazette*," says Jack quickly.

"I wrote that," Richardson tells him. "Brilliant, wasn't it?"

"Er …" Jack hesitates. "It wasn't true."

"Of course it was true," replies Richardson.

"The amount of money was wrong, nobody wanted Mr Howard's autograph, and Molly and I didn't say those things you wrote."

"You said 'thank you,'" says Richardson. "That's the same thing. Do you think I've got time to run around interviewing children? I'm a busy man. Go and play with your new PE equipment."

"That's what I wanted to tell you," says Jack. "It's all rubbish. The basketball is flat and the tennis racket is …"

"Are you trying to make me look stupid, Rico?"

"No. I just thought …"

"This morning," says Richardson, "I wrote that Dave Howard is a local hero. I'm not going to write the complete opposite tomorrow because of one popped basketball."

Without waiting for an answer, Richardson stomps back to his office.

"RICO SORRY IF VERONICA'S IN TROUBLE WITH BAD-TEMPERED BOSS," Jack says.

"I don't care," says Veronica. "He's always shouting. Any new job offer and I'm out of here."

"Good luck!"

"Thanks," says Veronica. "What about you? Where are you going next with your story?"

"Don't know," says Jack. "REPORTER HITS DEAD END."

"You can't think like that," Veronica tells him. "A reporter never gives up. Keep digging and see what you find."

"Where should I dig?"

"If it was me," says Veronica, "I'd take a trip to UltraGym."

Chapter 7

Day:	Wednesday
Time:	5:30 pm
Location:	UltraGym

"Welcome to UltraGym. My name is Sally. Would you like to join? You can swim, work out or simply chill at our juice bar."

Standing behind the reception desk, Sally wears a blue UltraGym uniform. She gives Jack exactly the same smile she gave to the previous ten people. Jack noticed that they all became members. Lots of them mentioned the article and said what a good man Dave Howard must be. Jack wonders what they'd think if they saw the broken PE equipment.

"Could I see Mr Howard?" asks Jack.

"Mr Howard is busy."

"I have a few things I want to ask him about the sports equipment he …"

The phone rings. "Excuse me a moment," says Sally.

Jack knows that you shouldn't listen in to other people's phone calls. But he isn't really listening. He's just standing nearby with his ears open.

"Hello, UltraGym." The caller says something. "I'm afraid Mr Howard is too busy to talk right now." The caller says something else. Loudly.

Sally winces. "Please don't shout at me, Mr Pribit. I didn't realise it was you. I'll connect you immediately." Sally puts the phone call through. Then she looks at Jack. "Swim, work out or chill?"

Jack doesn't answer. He's just remembered where he heard the name Pribit before – in the article about the swimming pool closing. Why is Mr Pribit phoning Mr Howard? And why does he get put through when nobody else does? "STRANGE GOINGS ON AT ULTRAGYM," thinks Jack.

Suddenly, out of his office comes
Mr Howard. Yesterday's big shark smile
has vanished.

"Key to the safe please, Sally," he snaps.

"Mr Howard," says Jack.

"I'm very busy."

"But I just have a few …"

"I *said,* I'm very busy." Mr Howard doesn't
even bother looking at Jack. Now that there
are no reporters around to take photos, he
doesn't need to be nice to a kid.

He grabs the key from Sally, picks up a backpack and goes over to the safe. Jack can see the big pile of banknotes inside. Mr Howard grabs a large handful and stuffs them into the backpack. "I'll be about an hour, Sally." Mr Howard pushes his way through the revolving doors and out into the street.

Sally watches him go. Then she remembers she has a customer. "Swim, work out or chill?"

But there's nobody to answer her question. Jack has gone.

Chapter 8

Day:	Wednesday
Time:	5:40 pm
Location:	Norton Park

Dave Howard charges down the main street, tightly clutching his backpack to his chest. He turns left at some traffic lights and then right soon after. He walks faster and faster, holding the backpack tighter and tighter. He's looking at everybody. After all, he's carrying a lot of money and someone might be a thief.

It makes it hard for Jack to follow him. He has to duck behind a wall, then hide behind a tree, then pretend to be bending over tying his laces.

When he looks up, there's no sign of Howard. Jack can't believe he's lost him. This could be his last chance to find out what's happening. He dashes down the street, his head darting frantically from side to side. Just in time, he spots Howard slipping into Norton Park. Jack's not going to lose him again. He sprints into the park.

Norton Park

PARK

Howard's walking towards the lake. The ducks start quacking, hoping for bread, but Howard ignores them. He goes straight to a bench, sits down and places the backpack next to him. There's another man already sitting there. He doesn't even look at Howard. Anybody passing by would think they were strangers just sharing a bench. But Jack isn't anyone. He remembers who the person is from the picture in Monday's paper: Arthur Pribit.

Jack hides behind a tree to see what happens. Nothing.

For five long minutes, Dave Howard and Arthur Pribit look at the ducks. Jack can't believe it. Are they both just birdwatchers?

Then, suddenly, without even glancing at Howard, Pribit leans over, picks up the backpack, looks inside, nods and puts it down next to himself. Howard, who'd been holding onto the backpack so tightly all the way to the park, doesn't even seem to notice. Weird.

Now, Jack can see that they're talking to each other. But not like people normally talk. They don't look at each other. Jack would give anything to be able to hear what they're saying. Maybe it's the key to breaking the story.

41

Then he remembers the mini-tape recorder! If he could just slip it under the bench, perhaps he could record what they're saying. But there's a problem. How can he get the tape recorder close enough without Howard and Pribit noticing? Jack needs an excuse to go scrambling behind the bench. And he hasn't got one. "BUDDING REPORTER WATCHES HELPLESSLY AS STORY SLIPS AWAY," sighs Jack.

Day:	Wednesday
Time:	5:55 pm
Location:	Norton Park

Suddenly, there's a shout behind Jack. Two boys are playing football. Jack has an idea.

He switches the tape recorder on and hides it in his hand. Then he pops out from behind the tree and jogs over to them. "Can I play?"

"OK," says one boy, kicking the ball over to him. "Pass it here."

Jack boots the ball as hard as he can towards the bench where Howard and Pribit are sitting.

The boy looks at him in disbelief. "That's the worst pass I've ever seen," he says.

"Sorry," says Jack. "I'll go and get it." Jack charges after the ball. He has to catch it before it goes past the two men. Jack runs faster than he's ever run before. He reaches the ball just as it rolls under the bench.

"What are you doing?" shouts Howard angrily.

"Sorry," says Jack, bending down to pick up the ball. He leaves the tape recorder in its place.

Chapter 11

Day:	Thursday
Time:	8:10 am
Location:	Jack Rico's house

There's a clunk as *The Daily World* plops onto the mat. Jack's mum picks it up and carries it into the kitchen. She's surprised to see Jack already sitting there eating his toast.

"Can I have a new bike?" asks Jack.

"It was 'no' on Monday. It's still 'no'. There's nothing you could say to convince me."

"How about if I say I'll buy it myself?"

His mum looks suspicious. "How would you get the money for a new bike?"

"SCHOOL BOY BREAKS MAJOR STORY IN NATIONAL NEWSPAPER," Jack answers.

His mum bursts out laughing. "Nice try, Jack," she tells him. "*The Daily World* is the biggest selling paper in the country. They don't take …" She glances at the front page and stops. "What's your name doing on this story?"

It's Jack's turn to laugh. He's laughing so hard he almost can't hear her reading the story out loud.

The Daily World

Swimming pool fraud

by Jack Rico

The Daily World has uncovered a disgraceful fraud in Norton. dishonest businessman, Mr David Howard, bribed health inspector, Mr Arthur Pribit, to fake results of a water-quality test to ensure the local swimming pool was closed down. Mr Howard hoped to

force people to join his expensive gym because there would be nowhere else in the area to swim. Howard and Pribit refused to comment. The police expect to make arrests later today.

The Daily World says: The sooner, the better.

Jack's mum puts down the paper. She's got a big smile on her face. "I guess we'll be going to the bike shop after school."

There's a knock on the front door. The phone rings at the same time.

"You do the door," says Jack's mum. "I'll do the phone."

Standing on the doorstep is Molly. "Want to walk to school?"

"I thought you were mad at me."

"Not since they re-opened the pool because of what you wrote," Molly tells him. "I've still got enough time to train to win the race."

"Jack," says his mum, appearing with the phone in her hand. "It's for you."

"Hello?" says Jack.

"Rico," says a familiar voice. "This is Mr Richardson from the *Gazette*. We've always been buddies, haven't we? I know I make jokes about your stories but I've always thought very highly of your ability."

"You never told me," says Jack.

"No," admits Richardson, "but I always thought it. And this story in *The Daily World* just shows how right I was. Anyway we're a bit short-staffed at the moment. Veronica's been offered a job on *The Daily World* out of the blue and she's taken it. So there's nobody to cover the swimming championship next week. I was wondering if you could do it for me."

"Hmmm," says Jack, "I'm quite busy."

"Please," begs Richardson. "I really need you."

EDITOR

"I suppose I can do it," Jack tells him. "After all, I've always wanted a story in the *Gazette*."

Jack hangs up the phone. "You sure you're going to win that race, Molly?"

Molly nods.

"So how do you want to be described in the *Gazette*?"

"What?"

Jack grins mischievously. "I was thinking 'lucky'."

"Lucky?" says Molly. "More like 'brilliant'!"

"Painfully slow?"

"Seriously fast!"

"Awkward?"

"Graceful!"

Still disagreeing, the two best friends set off for school.

CONTENTS

Author Camilla de la Bedoyere

who lives in a rainforest?

Rainforests are home to millions of animals and plants. People live there too. A place that is home to lots of animals and plants is called a habitat. Rainforests are very special habitats.

Draw

What kind of habitat do you live in? Draw a picture of it and colour it in.

which lizard can bark?

There are not many dogs in the jungle, but there are lizards that bark! They are called tokay geckos. Their bark sounds like 'to-kay, to-kay'. These lizards climb trees and hunt bugs at night.

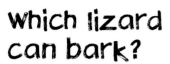
Macaws

Big mouth

Potoos are jungle birds that eat insects at night. They have big, gaping mouths and swallow their food whole.

why do parrots talk?

Parrots talk for the same reason we do – they need to tell each other things. When most parrots talk they twitter, screech and squawk. Some sounds are a warning. They tell other parrots that danger may be nearby.

Why do toucans have big bills?

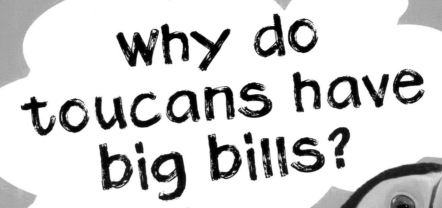

Toucans are birds with big, colourful bills (beaks). Both males and females have big bills, so they might be useful in attracting a mate. They may also help toucans reach and eat fruit high up in the trees.

Toucan

How big is a Goliath spider?

Goliath spiders are huge! They live in the rainforests of South America and can have a leg span of up to 30 centimetres. They eat insects and sometimes catch small birds to eat. Luckily, these spiders are harmless to people.

Goliath spider

Make

Use a paper plate, pipe cleaners and tape to make a life-size model of a Goliath spider.

Does it rain every day in a rainforest?

It rains almost every day in a rainforest. This habitat is home to plants that need lots of rain and plenty of hot, sunny days. Without rain and warmth, rainforest plants cannot grow.

Yum yum!

Leeches are slug-like animals that live in rainforest rivers. They love to suck blood from animals and humans!

which jungle cat has spots?

Jaguars are spotty jungle cats. Spots and stripes help animals to hide. Jaguars live in jungles and hide in trees and bushes. When they see or hear an animal they jump out and attack. Using colours and patterns to blend in is called camouflage.

Jaguar

Hide
Wear clothes that are a similar colour or pattern to your surroundings. How well hidden are you?

can lizards change colour?

Chameleons are lizards that can change colour. They may turn pink, red, green, blue, brown, yellow or even purple. Chameleons change colour when they are angry, or excited. They can also become the same colour as their surroundings.

Slime time!

Pitcher plants are bug-eating plants. Flies fall inside them, and get trapped in pools of liquid. The plants have slimy walls to stop flies escaping.

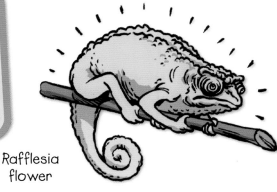

Rafflesia flower

what is the biggest flower?

The biggest flower is called rafflesia, and one bloom can grow to 90 centimetres wide – as wide as a table. Rafflesia flowers have thick, red petals and have a strong, bad smell that attracts insects to them.

which beetle is a giant?

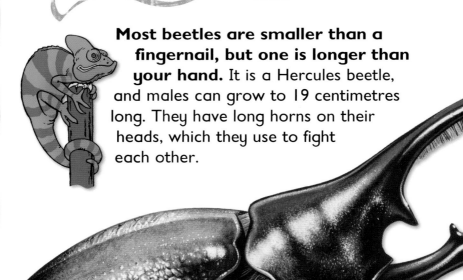

Most beetles are smaller than a fingernail, but one is longer than your hand. It is a Hercules beetle, and males can grow to 19 centimetres long. They have long horns on their heads, which they use to fight each other.

Hercules beetle

8

who has the strongest teeth in the jungle?

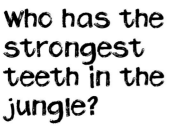

Agouti

Agoutis have such strong teeth they can bite through hard nut shells. Few animals are able to open the tough shells of Brazil nuts. Agoutis can bite through them to eat the tasty nut inside.

Big bird!

A cassowary is a bird, but it cannot fly. Cassowaries have sharp claws on their feet, and they kick out if they're scared by intruders.

Count

If an agouti eats five nuts every day, how many will it eat in two days?

can a piranha eat a horse?

No, a single piranha can't eat a horse, but a group, or shoal, could. Piranhas are fierce fish that live in some rainforest rivers, and they have very sharp teeth. When a group of piranhas attack, they can eat a big animal in minutes.

Do kangaroos live in trees?

Kangaroos don't live in trees – unless they're tree kangaroos! The furry tree kangaroo is small enough to climb trees and walk along branches. It sleeps in the day and feeds on leaves and flowers at night.

Tree kangaroo

What is a bird of paradise?

Birds of paradise are some of the most beautiful birds in the world. The males have fine feathers in many colours. Some birds grow long tail feathers. They show off their feathers to females when it is time to mate.

King bird of paradise

Raggiana bird of paradise

Princess Stephana's bird of paradise

Good-looking!

Quetzals are colourful jungle birds. Males grow long tail feathers that can reach one metre in length!

Draw

Draw a bird of paradise and decorate it using pens, glue and scraps of brightly coloured paper.

How do lizards fly?

Lizards cannot really fly because they don't have wings, but some lizards can glide. They have flaps of skin that they stretch out to glide through the air when they leap from a tree.

what is the biggest butterfly?

Millions of butterflies and moths flutter through the world's rainforests. One of the biggest is Queen Alexandra's birdwing butterfly. It can measure nearly 30 centimetres from wing tip to wing tip.

Queen Alexandra's birdwing butterfly

Why are jungle frogs so deadly?

Not all jungle frogs are deadly, but some have poisonous skin. Most poison-arrow frogs are small, and have colourful skin that is coated with poison. The golden poison-arrow frog is one of the deadliest of all, but it is no bigger than your thumb.

Golden poison-arrow frog

Sweet bird!

Hummingbirds feed on the sweet juice made by flowers. When they hover at a flower, their wings make a humming sound.

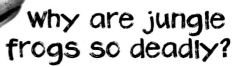

Who eats all the leaves?

The floor of the forest is covered with dead leaves. Some of them will rot away. Others will be eaten by the billions of tiny animals that live in a jungle — such as ants, caterpillars, slugs and snails.

Find

Look under plants and stones to see garden animals, such as ants, beetles, and woodlice. Try not to disturb them.

Are there dragons in the jungle?

There are no real dragons in the jungle, but there are lizards that look like dragons!
Boyd's dragon is an iguana that has a flap of skin under its chin, called a dewlap. It also has a row of spines that run along its back.

Boyd's → dragon

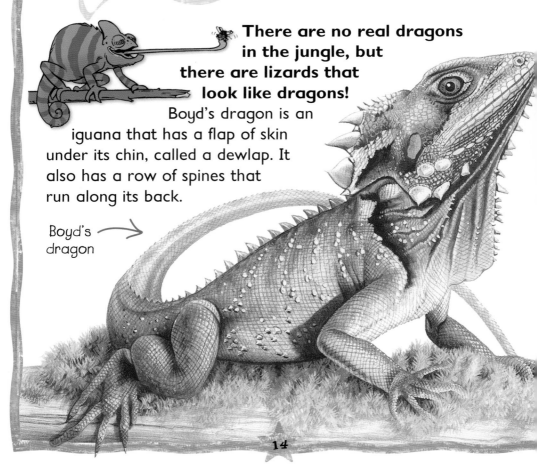

when is a leaf not a leaf?

When it is a leaf insect! Some rainforest insects pretend to be leaves or sticks. This means they can stay still and hide from birds and lizards that want to eat them. They also hide from other bugs they want to catch.

Leaf insect

yummy honey!

Sun bears have very strong claws for digging into bees' nests. They lick out the honey with their long tongues.

which bugs light up the night?

Glow insects do. Some of these bugs are called glow-worms and others are called fireflies. Hundreds of them gather in a tree, and twinkle like Christmas lights, or stars in the sky.

who lives in the clouds?

Gorillas live in cloud forests, where the tops of the trees are covered in mist and cloud. These rainforests are often wet and cool, but gorillas don't mind. They have thick fur, and spend most of the day eating leaves, playing and sleeping.

Baby gorilla

Red-eyed tree frogs

Which frog has scary eyes?

Red-eyed tree frogs use their big red eyes to scare enemies. If disturbed, the frogs flash their bulging eyes. This may startle predators and scare them away.

Find it

Use an atlas or the Internet to find the Amazon River in the Amazon rainforest. It's in South America.

Smashing chimps!

Clever chimps use stones as tools to crack open tough nuts and fruits.

Why do animals move home?

When part of a rainforest dies, or is cut down, the animals that live there move to find a new place to live. Every year, many animals lose their homes when people cut down trees in rainforests.

why are tigers stripy?

Stripes may help tigers to hide while they hunt. It is difficult to spot a striped animal hiding in the shadows. Tigers often crouch in long grass waiting for an animal to pass by. Then they pounce!

Tiger

can apes be orange?

Some apes are orange! Orang-utans are large apes that live in jungles in Asia. Their fur is long, and orange-brown. Baby orang-utans stay with their mothers until they are about 8 years old.

Mother and baby orang-utan

Think

Orang-utans are apes. Can you think of any other types of ape?

Do all birds live in trees?

Most birds live in trees, where they are safe from other animals. But some, such as the junglefowl, spend a lot of time on the ground. They find bugs, seeds and worms to eat there.

Giant frog!

Goliath frogs live in jungle rivers and lakes, and are big enough to swallow lizards. They can be more than 30 centimetres long!

Which bird is Lord of the Jungle?

The Philippine eagle is called the 'Lord of the Jungle'. It is one of the biggest birds in the world. This eagle has huge talons (claws) and a strong, curved bill. It hunts other birds, snakes, wild cats, lemurs and even monkeys.

Flying lemur

Philippine eagle

When is a toad like a leaf?

When it is hidden on the forest floor! Some jungle frogs and toads have colours and patterns that help them to hide on trees, leaves or branches. The leaflitter toad has brown camouflage that makes it look like a dead leaf.

Leaflitter toad

Tongue-twister!

Okapis have very long tongues. They are so long, an okapi can use its tongue to lick its eyeballs clean!

Why are some animals rare?

When the number of a species (type) of animal falls, it is said to be rare. Tigers, orang-utans and gorillas are rare. Animals become rare when they cannot find enough food, or their home in the wild has gone.

Think

Make up a story about three jungle animals and an adventure they have.

21

Why does a snake squeeze its food?

So it can eat it! The emerald tree boa is a rainforest snake. Once it has grabbed its prey, it wraps its body around it and squeezes it to death. This snake can grow to 2 metres long.

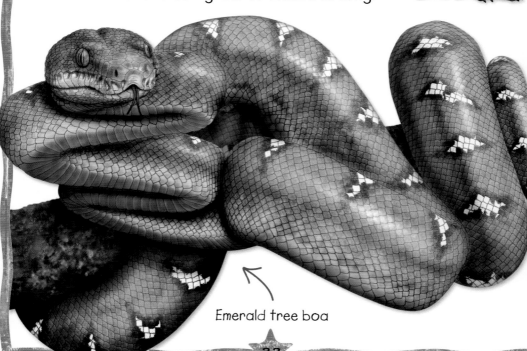

Emerald tree boa

Forest elephants

who has the biggest teeth in the jungle?

Elephants have the biggest teeth, called tusks. African forest elephants have tusks that point down, so they can walk through plants and trees without getting their tusks tangled in leaves!

Do monkeys have beards?

Mangabey monkeys have tufts of white hair that look like beards! These may help the monkeys to communicate. Mangabeys live in the Africa, in groups called 'troops'.

sticky toes!

Gecko lizards are able to crawl on rocks and trees because they have sticky toes. Tiny hairs on their toes work like glue, to make them stick.

23

Index

First published in 2005 by
Miles Kelly Publishing Ltd
Harding's Barn, Bardfield End Green,
Thaxted, Essex, CM6 3PX, UK

Copyright © Miles Kelly Publishing Ltd 2012

This edition published 2012

2 4 6 8 10 9 7 5 3 1

Publishing Director Belinda Gallagher
Creative Director Jo Cowan
Volume Design Redmoor Design
Cover Designer Jo Cowan
Image Manager Liberty Newton
Indexer Jane Parker
Production Manager Elizabeth Collins
Reprographics Stephan Davis,
  Thom Allaway, Lorraine King

ISBN 978-1-84810-902-5

Printed in China

British Library Cataloguing-in-Publication Data
A catalogue record for this book is
available from the British Library

ACKNOWLEDGEMENTS
All artwork from the Miles Kelly Artwork Bank

The publishers would like to thank the following
sources for the use of their photographs:
Fotolia.com 7 Jefery
Getty 18 Mitsuaki Iwago
Shutterstock.com 2 Juriah Mosin; 4 Eduarde
Rivero; 6 Ammit; 13 Eric Isselee; 15 Eric Isselee
16 Sam Chadwick; 19 Eric Gevaert;
23 Uryadnikov Sergey

All other photographs are from:
Corel, digitalSTOCK, digitalvision, John Foxx,
PhotoAlto, PhotoDisc, PhotoEssentials, PhotoPr
Stockbyte

Every effort has been made to acknowledge the
source and copyright holder of each picture.
Miles Kelly Publishing apologises for any
unintentional errors or omissions.

Made with paper from a sustainable forest

www.mileskelly.net
info@mileskelly.net

www.factsforprojects.com